Stay Safe While You Study

WELBECK
BALANCE

ABOUT THE AUTHOR

Dr Dominique Thompson is a family doctor (General Practitioner), young people's mental health expert, TEDx speaker, author and educator, with over 20 years of clinical experience caring for students, most recently as Director of Service at the University of Bristol Students' Health Service.

She is a Clinical Advisor for the Royal College of General Practitioners, and for Student Minds, the UK's student mental health charity. She was the family doctor for the NICE Eating Disorders' guidelines development group, and the Universities UK StepChange and Minding Our Future committees. Dr Thompson is also a member of the UK Mental Wellbeing in Higher Education group (MWBHE).

Dr Thompson's TEDx talk, "What I learnt from 78,000 GP consultations with university students", highlights some of the causes behind the recent rise in young people's mental health distress, and suggests ways in which everyone can better support the younger generation.

You can follow her on Twitter @DrDomThompson.

Stay Safe While You Study

Make the Most of Your Student Experience

DR DOMINIQUE THOMPSON

WELBECK
BALANCE

A Trigger Book
Published by Welbeck Balance
An imprint of Welbeck Publishing Group
20 Mortimer Street
London W1T 3JW

First published by Trigger Publishing in 2019.
Reprinted by Welbeck Balance in 2021

A CIP catalogue record for this book is available from the British Library.

ISBN
Trade Paperback – 978-1-80129-109-5
Typeset by Lapiz Digital Services
Printed in Great Britain by CPI Group (UK) Ltd, Croydon CRO 4YY

10 9 8 7 6 5 4 3 2 1

Note/Disclaimer

www.welbeckpublishing.com

For Jack.

A WHO'S WHO OF STUDENT SUPPORT

Family doctor

A family doctor is a medically qualified doctor who sees people in the community, not in a hospital. They are able to help with all conditions, although they may have a special interest, for example in skin problems or mental health. They are sometimes called GPs or general practitioners, and will often refer to specialists, such as psychiatrists or psychologists, for specific problems.

Counsellor

A counsellor offers a safe, confidential space for individuals to talk. Counsellors help their clients explore their thoughts, feelings and actions to help them come to terms with life and find more hopeful and useful ways to approach their future. Counsellors will work in different ways depending on their training, but will always allow their client to take the lead in what they want to talk about. They do not offer advice, but through the empathic attention they give to their client's words, the client often discovers their own wisdom, helping them to lead a more fulfilling life.

Clinical Psychologist

A person who specializes in psychological or emotional conditions and mental health disorders. They will have specialized in the study of clinical psychology and will usually have a doctorate or PhD (though they're not medically qualified and will not able to prescribe medication). They assess people and diagnose mental health conditions or problems. They are trained in using talking and behavioural interventions specifically tailored to treat psychological disorders. They may use a range of therapy approaches which vary from psychodynamic to cognitive behavioural therapy and family and couples' therapies, to interpersonal approaches. They base their assessment and treatment methods on scientific principles and outcomes, and will use the best evidenced method that helps to treat an individual.

Therapist

A term for professionals who use talking and behavioural therapies to support people with mental health conditions.

Psychiatrist

A medically qualified doctor who specializes in mental health conditions (also called psychiatric conditions) who can assess, make a diagnosis, offer advice, and prescribe medications. A psychiatrist is the only person who can prescribe some specialist medications. They work with family doctors, therapists, psychologists and counsellors, and will usually recommend a type of talking or behavioural treatment.

CONTENTS

INTRODUCTION

Many students, when asked, say they wish they had been better prepared for college (in the US) or university (in the UK) and had been given a more realistic idea of what to expect and how to look after themselves once there.

This book will help you prepare for the move to life in higher education (even if you will still be living at home, you will likely be moving to a different way of life) and prepare for some of the pressures and challenges that come with being a student.

The book will follow the timeline of a new student's experiences, starting with preparation before classes begin, and moving on to Welcome Week (known as Freshers' Week in the UK). It will then wind its way through the first and second halves of the year, taking into consideration the effect holidays can have. Finally, there will be a specific section on exams and assignments, which can cause students particular stress.

Throughout the book you will read comments and quotes from students and recent graduates about what they discovered, or wish they had known, about starting this chapter of life and looking after themselves.

Useful resources, websites, apps and further info can be found at relevant points along the way.

CHAPTER 1

PREPARING FOR FURTHER STUDY

> "I would have felt better prepared if there was not such an expectation for uni to be the best part of your life."

This quote, from a student who took part in a survey in 2018, sums up the feelings of so many students. It's often said that university years are the best years of your life, but it's fair to say that – while it's hoped that these years are a positive experience – they are *rarely* the best of anyone's life! They involve significant hard work, they are tiring, and they are *often* a lot of fun. But not always.

It's important to have a more realistic view of these years. They are a path to useful qualifications and they give you an opportunity to try new things, meet new people, be yourself, and discover independence. But they are also academically challenging, exhausting, financially strained, testing of your patience (often with friends, flatmates and relationships), and highly pressured. You need to step onto that path ready for highs and lows, and also ready to bounce back when the going gets tough.

Here's another quote from that survey:

"It's okay to have ups and downs during your studies. Having downs doesn't mean you've failed."

TOP TIP FOR ADDRESSING PRE-ARRIVAL WORRIES

If you have specific worries, sit down with a trusted friend or family member and make a list of them. Then work through them and address those worries together. It may help to put the different worries into categories, such as "money", "socializing", or "living away from home", and then make an action plan for each one (Thompson and Cole-King, 2018). For more top tips like these, see the end of the book.

What Do Teachers Think?

"Secondary-school students are too *focused* on short-term grades and academic results and *unable* to *visualize* life at university."

This was the conclusion of a study of UK teachers in 2017, who were worried about their pupils being unprepared for university life, but were keen to help them get ready (Hughes, Massey, Williams, 2017).

Does that sound like you when you were in your last year of secondary school? Were you almost entirely focused on the next week's grades or exam results, and just assuming that any next steps would work themselves out?

Hopefully, this book will help you to think ahead, *visualize* what life might be like, consider potential problems, and plan your response in advance. This will better equip you to ride the waves of those testing but exciting times ahead.

Let's start with health issues.

Health Issues and Avoiding "Magical Thinking"

Doctors in college or university health centres get pretty used to seeing students who arrive with the hope that their medical issues, particularly mental health issues, will somehow go away as they start their new lives.

It is very common for students to long for this (somewhat miraculous) situation. That their issues should suddenly fade into the background – the anxiety that plagued their qualification exams, the obsessive-compulsive behaviours that made them late for everything, the eating issues that ruined their social lives before they arrived – is a wonderful and understandable thing to wish for. But sadly, it rarely (if ever) happens.

This means that doctors regularly see a significant number of students who find themselves, about four or six weeks into the first term, struggling with their new life and academic pressures. They may also be desperate for help as their previous issues, which they have tried to ignore or move on from, rear their ugly heads once more.

In a few cases, the symptoms become bad enough to cause the students to suspend studies (take a "leave of absence") soon after arrival. This is a real shame for them – with a little planning in advance and coordination of healthcare, the need to put their studies on hold so soon could perhaps be avoided.

So let's be really clear at this point, so that you can start uni life as you mean to go on ... *feeling and functioning well*.

If you had mental health or emotional issues *before* starting university, certainly in the two or three years immediately prior, then you are very likely to have similar or related issues *after* starting, or when your stress levels rise. So it is better to discuss this in advance, continue any medication and therapy, and *not suddenly stop treatment and support*. It does not have to stop you having a good and successful time. Dealing with the issues up front is going to help; ignoring them is likely to make things worse. We want to avoid this situation.

From yet another student in my survey:

> "I knew I'd need help before I arrived, but I left it far too late. Now I'm still on the waiting list for treatment."

PRE-ARRIVAL HEALTH CHECKLIST

1. Book an appointment with your usual doctor at home before heading off to university, to discuss your health issues. Arrange a letter to take (they can provide a printout of your health record summary) in case there is a delay in records switching between home and university doctors.

2. If you are under the care of a specialist doctor, ask them to refer you to the specialist team in your new location or discuss with them when you see them for follow-up during the holidays. Again, a summary letter can be helpful to take with you (emailed to you so you can forward it to the new doctor). If you are currently in active psychological treatment, you will need to find an appropriate professional to continue your therapy. Alternatively, you may be able to continue with your current therapist via video call, or book in sessions during term breaks. You may also be able to have some sessions which aim to prepare you for your uni life.

3. If you receive medications, medical devices, or equipment that may be difficult to obtain in your new town, plan ahead so that you have plenty of supplies (two months' worth is standard) and know how to get more. For example, in the UK, family doctors cannot prescribe some medications for ADHD (Attention Deficit Hyperactivity Disorder); they can only be prescribed by specialist doctors, so problems can arise when a student runs out and has to go without, because their new doctor isn't a specialist and can't prescribe them. This is also an

issue for international students arriving in a country where their medications do not exist or are not licensed. This can include contraceptive pills, psychiatric medication and allergy medications. Plan ahead!

4. Before arriving at your new place of study, check out their website's "health and wellbeing" section (sometimes called "student support") to see what they recommend for resources relevant to your health issues. Connect with the disability team if you have known physical or mental health problems, to see if you are eligible for financial or practical help (government money is sometimes available). Talk to your university's wellbeing teams in advance of arrival.

5. On arrival in your new "home", register with a local doctor. This may mean filling in your details online or completing a paper form for the practice. The university may have a health team on campus, or they may recommend a local doctor with whom they have links. Ask other students which doctors they recommend. If the practice is not a student-specific one, ask the receptionist if any of the practitioners have a particular interest in student or young adult health, or in the health condition that you have (for example, diabetes or ulcerative colitis).

6. Try to make the call to register or book an appointment with them yourself. If you are anxious about this, ask a trusted person to sit next to you as you make the call. They could even go with you to your first appointment.

7. Take a small first-aid kit with you to your residence hall. Put in some plasters,

painkillers, dressings and paper tape, paper stitches, etc., and make sure you know how to use or take them. Be prepared! If you're sexually active you should also take condoms or another birth control method with you.

8. If you are not used to getting prescriptions or buying over-the-counter medications such as for flu, colds or allergies, then familiarize yourself with the basics, wander round a pharmacy, and ask friends or family how the prescription process works.

9. If you're not familiar with the healthcare system where you'll be living, read a bit about it on your institution's website, or read a leaflet for international students on how it all works. In the UK, healthcare is managed through the National Health Service or NHS (visit nhs.uk). In the US, you may need insurance or your university may provide services at a reduced cost – check their website or welcome packet for information.

10. Check which immunizations (vaccines) are recommended before arrival, for example, those against mumps, measles, rubella, or meningitis. Get yourself immunized before you move in with several hundred students from all over the world, who may be unwitting carriers of infection, and differently immune to you! Take a copy of all your immunizations with you.

11. Have a dental and eye test before you leave home. Once you're in the swing of things you won't want to worry about eyes and teeth, and it may prevent issues arising when you're living a busy student life.

In Summary

Preparation is key to ensuring as smooth a start to life in higher education as possible. There are loads of things you can do to prepare in advance of arrival – some of which you may never have considered before, or which may seem obvious or common sense – but often, in the excitement and rush of heading off, they can be forgotten. Some, such as vaccinations, can even be potentially lifesaving.

So make a list, check it through with trusted friends and family, and get yourself ready for transition to your new life!

CHAPTER 2

ESSENTIAL LIFE SKILLS

So now that you've got your healthcare taken care of (and if you don't look after your health, you're unlikely to be able to enjoy the rest of your experience as much as you might), let's think about other things you might need to think about to prepare for your new adventure.

Cooking 101

People who work in universities often say they are amazed at how few secondary school pupils or new students can cook. Yet it is a basic survival skill. The story of the newly arrived student who blew up the hall of residence's kitchen on day one, having tried to microwave a *whole* can of beans (yes, including the can!) is a perfect illustration of what can happen when someone with no idea what they're doing suddenly has to "cook".

A simple plan here might be to learn three or four of your favourite, but basic, tasty dishes from scratch (for example, spaghetti Bolognese, roasted chicken, scrambled eggs, or veggie stirfry) before you come to uni or when you know you are going to need to cook for yourself and friends. Then you can rely on these to get you through the first few opportunities to cook while learning a few more from other people, TV programmes, blogs or recipe books along the way.

A great piece of advice to keep you reasonably healthy if you *do* have to rely on some convenience foods is to try to make a meal every few days that "doesn't have any labels" – in other words, using fresh or individual ingredients rather than ready meals or fast food.

Laundry

Another story from week one at university is from a student who watched as a fellow first year emptied half a box of laundry detergent into the machine she was using to wash her clothes. It was clear the student had never done her own laundry before and had no idea how much of the soap to use (a small cupful, in case you're interested). Comedy bubbles and frothing from the machine ensued, but it wasn't a great start to independent life!

Simply being familiar with washing machines, laundrettes, or the basics of washing and ironing can be really useful once you are on your own and having to look after your clothes. Clearly, many young people have done their own laundry from a young age, but not all, so this is a nudge to think about it!

Financial Skills

You don't need to be a money expert to know that money can have a significant impact on people's health and wellbeing. Therefore, it is important to have a basic idea about how to budget sensibly from day one, and it's definitely worth considering how you might earn some extra money while studying or during the holidays. Of course, with some full-time courses it is not possible to study, rest *and* have a job, but a bit of bar work, restaurant work, babysitting or dog walking for faculty members may help earn a little cash – and holiday jobs are definitely possible.

For expert budget advice it is worth looking at dedicated websites and reading articles written by professionals. There are some examples in the resources at the end of this book.

Being money-smart may not sound cool, but you will definitely feel less stressed (and a tiny bit smug!).

Becoming Independent

You may only be reading this book as you arrive for your first term, but if you have a chance to think about this one prior to arrival, then this is the time to get yourself ready to be independent from your parents.

The last year or two before leaving home is a good time to start to prepare for your new life. One example is to use public transport or a bike to get around, rather than expecting your parents or guardians to drive you everywhere. Even if they offer, it's okay to say "No thank you" and tell them you'll catch the bus, walk, or cycle when it's safe to do so. If you have the opportunity to learn to drive, it's worth doing it even if you don't have your own car for a while. It's a great skill to have and it's considered by many employers to be an essential skill. It will make you feel independent, and pretty impressed with yourself for getting on and doing it.

Open Days

Although it's now common for parents to go along to open days, consider going on your own. It's your life, and where you go and what you study is your choice. There may be situations which require you to involve parents or guardians – or you may simply want to involve them anyway – but ensure that the decisions you take are yours.

Arrival

Once you do arrive on the first day of term, encourage family to drop you off but not to hang around with you for too long. Perhaps encourage them to go for a cup of tea or coffee, have a walk around, or visit the campus without you. But they should let you get on with things – meet people, do your own first shop or make your bed yourself – as that is an important way to establish your new independence. Encourage your parents not to stay and use any "parent accommodation" that might be provided by the halls of residence, unless they have an exhausting journey requiring a stopover.

A good tip from another student, to ease the initial introductions to new friends or room-mates, is:

> "Take games or biscuits; something you can share with other people and socialize with."

Another great tip is not to go home for the first four weeks of university, otherwise you will miss out on lots of early bonding time, parties, sitting chatting in people's rooms or lounges and early events with clubs and societies. You might feel a bit down or lonely, but try to push through and chat with people. Speak to family and friends at home but aim to stay on campus, so that you feel part of your new community.

Contacting Home

It's entirely normal to want to stay in touch with family and friends from home once you arrive at university, but it may be worth discussing the frequency of such contact before you leave, especially with parents or guardians, as they may have an expectation of how often you will check in, which might differ from yours. This avoids misunderstanding and he possibility of them calling the police when you don't text or WhatsApp them every 24 hours because you're sleeping off the effects of Welcome Week, or possibly with a new-found "friend" from the night before. (The police scenario has definitely happened!)

Agreeing frequency of contact (and which format that will take – will it be text, call, Messenger, Facebook?) is key here, so be clear. It's best *not* to agree to be in contact every 24 hours or more often anyway, as this allows for unexpected changes in timetables, activities, trips, sleep patterns and so on. Something along the lines of a message every other day, and a call once or twice a week, might be a good balance. It's up to you, but plan it in advance to avoid parental stress and calls to the authorities when you are late checking in.

In Summary

Some of these life or "independent living" skills may be things you have been doing for years, and others may be completely new to you, but they can make all the difference to settling in and staying on top of things. Once academic work starts and the deadlines become real, you will be super focused on those and on going out and enjoying your new social life, so you won't want to be worrying about food or laundry! Make sure you are in charge of your money, social and transport needs, so that you can relax and have a good time.

CHAPTER 3

WELCOME WEEK

This is a big week.

Welcome Week has assumed almost legendary and somewhat overwhelming status over the decades, which can feel like a huge pressure for new students. Not only are you *supposed* to be making "friends for life" and starting a course that could "transform your future", but you're expected to have the *best time ever* with loads of people you don't know, in a new place, while being the best version of yourself. It's exhausting!

So let's see what the reality is really like and what recent students have said about Welcome Week, or "Fresher's" as it is often called in the UK. It may help to put things into perspective.

TOP TIPS FOR WELCOME WEEK

- You will be hit with a whole lot of new information. Make a note of the important things, such as where your room is, where you eat, where you need to register for your course, where you need to register for healthcare, and where the student advice or support centre is.
- Add important new contacts and emergency numbers to your phone and get a sense of the bus routes or cycle paths.
- Walk around the relevant bits of campus so that you become familiar with them before lectures start.

- Find out where to do laundry and where the residence/accommodation staff can be found if needed (where to enquire about security, new lightbulbs, or to sort broken furniture, etc.).
- Go along to welcome meetings, as a lot of useful info is given out in one place.
- If you haven't had all your relevant immunizations (meningitis or MMR vaccines) by now, then they will be available somewhere nearby, like at the local doctor, so go and have them. It may literally save your life.
- Register with the doctor when you're there too, if you haven't already done this.
- Check where the counselling and support services are, even if you don't need them. You or your friends might at some point.

The *sensory overload* that is common in Welcome Week can be particularly overwhelming for some students who are sensitive to this, such as those with Asperger's syndrome (a type of autism spectrum disorder) or social anxiety, so don't worry if this is you. Just take it slowly, sit quietly at the back, listen, and take it all in – in your own time and at your own pace. Then have breaks if you need them, but try not to avoid everything or you will miss out.

And one of the best bits of student advice for everyone: It is okay to say no to things, or to explain that you need time to yourself as well.

Welcome (or Fresher's) Fair

This is one tradition worth checking out: the opportunity to see all the clubs, societies, and organizations that the student union offers, alongside entertainment/gigs and a chance to find out what your new home is all about.

Advice from some students includes: "Join clubs and societies – they're full of like-minded people and making friends there is easier than on your course" and "To meet new people initially, you may have to try things that you might not end up enjoying, for example joining the frisbee club!"

Resist the temptation to sign up for everything, but take care not to go the other way and only join groups that are good for your CV or résumé. Give the "fun" clubs like the Chocolate Society, or knitting groups, a chance too.

Most people do have periods of feeling lonely, and it is important to get involved with societies and non-academic interests early on. Studying is a fantastic opportunity to meet people and try new things – it's not just an academic tick box; it's also a whole new world of opportunity! You might discover you have a natural talent for Quidditch, Ultimate Frisbee, journalism, or another activity you have never tried. You might even have a passion for cheese (yes, there are cheese-focused groups!) or barbershop singing.

Maybe approach the fair with the plan to join one activity you know you will like and have tried before, and one thing you have never tried, or always wanted to … just don't spend all your time (or money, if applicable) joining clubs on day one!

Take time out if needed. Don't forget that if it's all getting a bit much, you can have a break and sit quietly in your room to have some time alone. Or you could sit with a few friends and just chat, eat some snacks and get to know each other.

Initiation Rites and Ceremonies

Most universities have outlawed these ceremonies, which were usually related to sports clubs or specific courses (or to fraternities and sororities, in the US). However, it is fair to assume that many may have gone "underground" and you may still be invited to take part or witness them. The strong message here is steer clear (or fake an illness, allergy or medical condition)!

Unless they are a gentle introduction to the rest of the team or your course-mates (which is not likely!) then they usually involve significant amounts of alcohol and regrettable, if not highly unsanitary, behaviour. For example, there have been cases that have involved crawling though disgusting muck to get to a beer at the end – resulting in terrible stomach problems in the new students.

Peer pressure can be a terrible thing, but it's just fine to take a deep breath, say "No, thanks" and walk away. You won't be the only one who feels like that, and hopefully you won't be the only one to make your voice heard.

In the most serious cases that you may have read about in the media, students have died as a consequence of excessive alcohol or mixing different alcohols in large volumes. They have even drowned on their way home by falling into local rivers and canals. Initiation ceremonies rarely end well. Bear this in mind when making up your mind about whether or not to get involved.

Partying

> "There's nothing wrong with not wanting to go out all the time, and many people also feel this way."

This is one of the most obvious pressures of Fresher's, or Welcome Week, with club nights and special events competing for your attention. You don't have to say yes to everything. Again, the key here is moderation.

Pick a couple of events that really appeal and go with some new people as an opportunity to get to know them. See whether they share your sense of what a good time is and whether they share your taste in music. Go home when you want to; don't feel you have to stay if you're not having fun. Clubbing or partying isn't for everyone; there are other ways of making friends.

New Friends and Relationships

One of the best bits of advice from the student survey was this: "Don't get pulled into intense relationships early on. You might not even meet your long-term friends until after Christmas." In other words, don't make "panic friends"!

Be friendly, sure, but don't feel you have to be best friends with everyone you meet. Who knows who your "forever

"Take breaks and be patient. Be patient with finding your 'place' at university and with finding friends. It's better to wait for those genuine and good friendships rather than panicking and forming and holding on to friendships that shouldn't be there. There are so many people at university and you don't have to change anything about yourself to fit in with people who aren't really a good fit. Wait for those you just click with."

friends" will be, or even if you will stay in touch with any of these people once you're not studying together anymore. Some people form strong friendships during this time; others form relaxed relationships but make much closer friends in their place of work, or when they travel, join a sports club, or have children later in life, for example.

As one student said, "Do not give in to the fear of missing out simply to be part of the crowd. You will eventually find people you get along with by being true to yourself."

Take your time to get to know lots of people, don't allow your social circle to be too narrow, and say yes to new offers to meet up and go out, as long as you feel comfortable with that person. And if anyone acts "off" towards you because you are making other new friends and not just spending time with them, be very careful – they may be overly demanding and "needy" of you.

This goes for new romantic relationships too.

Romance

Falling in Fresher love ...

It is common to fall in love in Welcome Week! The sheer number of cute new people to meet is impressive, and an easy trap to fall into is a co-dependent relationship with your new partner, where you become inseparable while everyone else is making lots of new friends. This may cause problems for you later, if or when the new relationship breaks down, as they often do. You will be left with few friends to support you when everyone else has connected and settled into new social groups.

So take your time. Meet and maybe date people, but don't get too committed too quickly, either to new friends or boy/girlfriends.

And remember, there will be downs as well as ups at the beginning. We will talk more about loneliness later on in the book. Be prepared that you will, from time to time, feel sad and lonely. This will pass.

Alcohol

When students were asked what they had to say about drinking and alcohol in Welcome Week (and beyond!) there were two sides to their responses.

"Be prepared for the drinking culture," one student suggested. Another said, "It would have been useful to dispel the myths about drink and drugs that a lot of people like to think is normal for Fresher's Week."

In other words, there is clearly an emphasis on drinking and this culture can be quite forceful during Welcome Week in particular, but it may not be as bad as you expect. If it is there, you may be able to avoid it – or handle it – better than you think.

The fact of the matter is that young people simply don't drink as much alcohol as previous generations did. In fact, according to a recent survey by the UK's National Union of Students about 1 in 5 students is now teetotal (doesn't drink alcohol at all). Universities are recognizing this trend and have responded by providing alcohol-free halls of residence in many UK and US cities. You might want to consider this, regardless of whether or not you drink, to ensure a calmer, quieter place to live and study.

So, as you start this new chapter, you may find it possible to be careful with your alcohol intake – or choose not to drink – with less peer pressure than you expected and with more students choosing to be moderate like you.

Don't be afraid to be yourself and say when you've had enough or say "No, thanks" if you don't want any at all.

And if you are going to drink, then this is a great piece of advice too:

> "If you're going to be drinking a lot, then make sure you're balancing that with looking after your physical health in other ways, such as sleeping, exercising, and eating well."

If you *are* going to drink, try to spread your intake over the week rather than having a lot on one or two evenings a week (binge drinking). You may like to space out your drinking evenings and not drink every night. You can try alternating your drinks, having a non-alcoholic one between alcoholic drinks. Pace yourself and try to really reduce your drinking around exam times, as it can interfere with memory retention, learning and sleep, all of which are crucial for academic success.

Sex: A Word About Condoms ...

The latest generation of students and young adults has been really impressive in reducing their use of alcohol, cigarettes and drugs. They have also significantly reduced unplanned pregnancies, which is great. What hasn't been so reassuring is the rising number of certain sexually transmitted infections (STIs).

Every autumn term, student health centres unfortunately see quite a lot of young people a few weeks after Welcome Week who got carried away in the excitement of "meeting" new people and who then need to be tested for sexual infections. Other times they are subsequently contacted by someone they "met" in Welcome Week advising them to get treatment too, as that person has now been diagnosed with an STI!

So it seems that, while people *are* thinking about safe sex in terms of not getting pregnant and relying on pills, injections, coils and implants to achieve this, condoms *aren't* getting as much attention. The consequence is rising numbers of gonorrhoea and syphilis infections (Waters, 2018), which is bad news for your generation's fertility. It also causes unpleasant symptoms (and some other potentially long-term complications).

According to Public Health England, the most at-risk groups for STIs are heterosexual 15- to 24-year-olds, black or ethnic minorities, and gay, bisexual, or other men who have sex with men. Similarly, the Centers for Disease Control and Prevention (CDC) in the US noted that 2019 was the sixth year in a row in which STIs increased overall, with half of all new cases occuring in people aged 15 to 24. So please *use condoms*!

There are many places to get tested, most of them for free, so doctors and national experts strongly recommend an *annual check-up* for all STIs! Search online or ask at a pharmacy to find local free testing for STIs in your area. Some will offer postal kits too, which is even easier. Alternatively, ask the nurses at your local doctor or student health centre for advice.

In Summary

"It's important to know that if you don't like Welcome Week, then that doesn't make you weird or mean there's something wrong with you. It doesn't mean that you're not cut out for university. It's so normal — you're in a new place, doing a new subject, forced into new friendships with people you may or may not like at all ... it takes time to settle in, but the perception is that you're supposed to have the most amazing time from day one."

Welcome Week can be great fun, but it can also be hectic and tiring, so try to pace yourself and listen to your instincts. There will be a lot to take in: loads of new information, the temptation to join millions of societies and to say yes to everything. Don't feel you have to be friends with everyone; exert some self-control when you need or want to around drink, drugs and sex, and make sure you look after yourself in what can be an exhausting and overwhelming few days!

CHAPTER 4

FINDING YOUR FEET

Let's hear from some of those students again, this time on the subject of balancing academic work with social activities ...

Getting into Your Studies

> "Go to every single lecture; it feels worse if you stay in all day doing nothing and the stress of missing out on new material piles up fast."

> "Don't do too much, but also don't allow yourself to be isolated — go to events and meet people. Do your work but then find something you enjoy for yourself."

Starting life in higher education means many things, but importantly, of course, it means learning a new subject or developing a deeper knowledge of a favourite area. This will likely involve discovering new *ways* to learn, as well as adapting to a different level of flexibility and freedom to study when and how you like.

Although class attendance is, in many institutions, loosely monitored, this is not like school or having a job – where if you don't show up, various measures will be put in place. In those circumstances, people will spring into action to find you and find out what's going on. But here, technology allows you to study from your room, review the material later online, and also, of course, link up with people from your course to catch up on lost work.

There are obvious pros and cons to all of this freedom and autonomy, but what the students quoted here are stating, from their own experiences, is to try to keep up as you go along for your own sake, to keep your stress to a minimum. But if you *do* need a day off to recover or rest, then take it, because presenteeism (turning up when you're ill and should be at home) is bad for you too.

It can take time to adapt to the new pace of work. You might be given a term to write an essay, for example, or a year to do a project and write it up (and often in groups), and this is where you will need to try to see what works for you.

It's best not to leave everything until the last minute, of course, but it is proven to be better to work on longer-term projects gradually, coming back to them a few times, allowing ideas to percolate through your brain where possible, rather than trying to sit down and write it all at once. The evidence for this and more, if you're interested in knowing about effective and efficient ways that we learn, is in an excellent book by Benedict Carey called *How We Learn*. It is well worth a look!

Group Work

Working in groups brings its own stresses, and students commonly say that this is one of the skills that they struggle with most, because of the need to adapt to other people's approaches to work, deadlines and responsibility. Do the others take a fair share of the work? Are they control freaks, or do you not see them from one week to the next? These are all common scenarios in group work.

Many universities offer study skills classes and opportunities to discuss such challenges, so it might well be worth asking your academic tutor or support staff about these. There are also some excellent books for students that address this; see the resources page for suggestions.

Finding Your "Tribe"

In and among the work, of course, is the opportunity to meet new people from all over the world, and with whom you might form deep and long-lasting friendships over shared political or social views. Maybe at secondary school you always felt like the odd one out, but at university, many people find that they finally connect with others like them. They meet their "tribe" and it can be very fulfilling and affirming to feel connected to others in this way.

Take your time to chat to lots of different people, and perhaps take up opportunities to socialize through your course as well as in the more traditional ways, to maximize your opportunities to meet people.

> "Try lots of things. Go out and meet as many people as possible in the first few weeks, then you can choose who to stick with."

Loneliness

Of course, it's also true that it can seem very difficult to meet people or make friends in this huge new environment, with so many strangers and too many opportunities to choose from.

> "The hardest things were not immediately having a stable group of friends to rely on and sometimes being in unavoidable but uncomfortable situations, as well as feelings of loneliness and sometimes isolation, especially to start with."

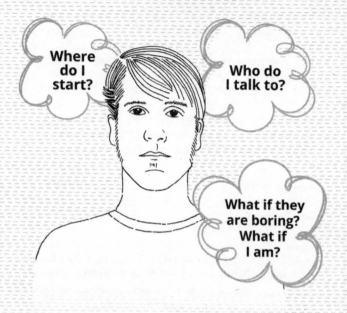

All these questions and more flood through your brain.

It can seem like the easiest thing in the world to retreat to your room, go online, chat to friends and family on your phone, and ignore the new and seemingly "scary" outside world. But this is not a great option. If at all possible, I would suggest you try to venture out. Start by walking around, smile at people who seem friendly in safe places like the lecture theatre or residential shared spaces. Then maybe build up to starting a conversation about something you will likely have in common, like the lecturer or your course.

And don't forget to exercise and get out and about. Make sure you explore your new home area.

TOP TIPS TO START A CONVERSATION

Try these conversation starters:

- "What do you think of the course so far?"
- "Where did you live before university?"
- "That lecturer seems nice; have you heard much about them?"
- "What do you think of the food here?"
- "Have you joined any of the teams or societies yet?"

These are gentle opening questions that allow you to see how someone will respond, whether they smile, and whether they are chatty or anxious or grumpy. And just like that, you will have pushed back against becoming isolated and lonely.

International Students

For international students there can be particular hurdles involved with arriving in a new country, experiencing a foreign culture and a different time zone to your family and friends, and sometimes managing all of this in a new language while trying to study a challenging academic subject.

I have known of students staying up every night to video call home at 3am, as that is the only time their families can speak. I've also known of students dealing with civil war back home. Both are very different scenarios, but both can cause real alienation from other students, who are not having to cope with such difficulties or trauma.

There are usually excellent services and support options available for international students, provided by staff teams or the student union. They can help you to feel less isolated and alone and they are ready to help with everything from visa issues to day trips, academic challenges or health concerns. Look for the International Student Office or team. There are also increasing numbers of websites and resources specializing in international student support. It can help to link up with other overseas students through societies and the student union or international organizations in the city or town you live in. You are not alone!

Students with Communication or Social Skills Challenges

Trying to make friends and meet new people can be particularly daunting if you are not naturally inclined that way or if you have disabilities. Students with social anxiety or autism spectrum diagnoses – as well as many others – can find the constant pressure to chat, make small talk, connect with others, and generally be sociable quite overwhelming.

Some initial top tips on taking steps towards meeting new people might include:

- Have a trusted person you can talk things through with
- Test out conversation topics with them
- Run through scenarios with them
- Get them to check in on how you're doing

Meeting people through shared interests or hobbies is always a winner, so the Welcome Week fair might feel a bit hectic. But it should give you some ideas of societies and clubs that might suit you.

Other good opportunities to meet like-minded people are through sports teams, volunteering or, of course, online – wherever you feel you can be yourself. You don't need a huge circle of friends, just a few good ones who you can rely on. Don't give up; it may take a few attempts to meet them but it will be worth it.

You are *not* alone, however much you may occasionally feel it, and however "different" you may feel. There are good people out there who are keen and eager to help you. Please reach out and connect.

Remember, the staff are very aware of the risks of isolation, so they will be planning and arranging loads of activities for students, such as treasure hunts, pub/trivia quizzes, movie nights and so on. Some of these will not involve alcohol, which allows for different people to meet others with shared interests. Join any of these that might interest you, especially if they allow you to become part of a team in some way. A good example is a quiz, which is always a great avenue to get to know people without having to have a direct conversation.

"It's okay to not be having fun all the time, even if it looks like everyone else is. Getting involved somehow, whether that be through societies or through your course or through volunteering, is a great way to make friends and also give yourself a sense of purpose and a routine."

Accommodation – What if You Hate It?

Where we live is absolutely crucial to our wellbeing as humans. Living in a tiny, cramped, damp space with horrible views is soul destroying, as is being unable to sleep because of noisy neighbours or being so far from all your friends and course-mates that you can't easily join in activities. It doesn't have to be this way!

So, if you are unhappy with where you are living and it's negatively affecting your emotional wellbeing, talk to the university office or a student union team that deals with these issues. If you are in private residence halls, speak to the in-house manager or landlord. Make your case and see what your options are. It may not be straightforward, but there are always options, and in the first term especially there can be other students moving around or coming and going, so spaces may crop up that weren't there on arrivals day. The key here is to *talk* to someone about it in the accommodation office or private provider's office. Don't suffer in silence.

Food and Weight Issues

Arriving at university, there is sometimes a choice to be made about catering options, especially in the UK; you can usually choose catered or self-catering residences. This is clearly a personal decision, and you will need to weigh up the pros and cons of each, whether those are based on social, financial or dietary needs.

Student health centre staff, who are caring for thousands of students, are aware that this decision could have quite important implications for both physical and mental health. For example, if you have medical conditions requiring a special diet, such as gluten free, you will need to weigh up the cost of buying the food yourself versus asking the residence to provide it for you in your accommodation. Or, students with eating disorders might choose to live in self-catered halls, but then not actually make themselves sufficient food, leading to rapid deterioration. Neither of these scenarios are about right or wrong, they just illustrate the personal nature of this decision and the need to take time to consider your options.

It is also important not to underestimate the time it can take to shop for food or cook for yourself. Learn to cook a few meals so that you can invite friends over, or just stay healthy! Resorting to fast food or deliveries and snacks can prove both expensive and unhealthy.

For students with eating issues, this new culinary independence can lead to challenges with staying healthy or even occasionally a deterioration in their eating. As such, if you notice this within yourself or a friend, it is important to seek advice and help without delay.

In Summary

Challenges in the first half of the school year may come from accommodation issues, friendships and academic pressures. All of these can be overcome with some help from others, including the university's professional teams. Try to find a work–life balance and find some like-minded friends.

CHAPTER 5

STAYING SAFE AND WELL

Personal Safety

Keeping yourself safe during your studies is perhaps something that is lower down your list of things to think about, but it is, of course, vitally important. It can be easy to get lost in the "bubble" of studying and forget that there are some dangers both inside and outside of that bubble.

Drink "spiking" – where someone else puts a substance in your drink (such as one of the "date rape" drugs or sleeping pills) so that you become woozy, sleepy and vulnerable to being taken advantage of or assaulted – is unfortunately a risk, and well worth being alert to.

TOP TIPS FOR AVOIDING DRINK SPIKING

With some basic awareness and measures taken, you can protect yourself and still have a great night out:

- Never leave your drink unattended
- Never accept drinks from people unless you have watched them being poured
- Never let the drink out of your sight
- Cover your bottled drinks with your thumb or use a specially designed drink stopper that you can drink through with a straw

It is absolutely not your fault if your drink gets spiked, but it is sensible to try to reduce the risk. And if you think that you may have been at the receiving end of such a thing because you feel more drunk or woozy than you should, then tell a reliable friend or call someone you trust to take you home straight away. Do *not* try to go home alone.

In terms of general safety when walking around or getting home at night, make sure you use reputable local transport, such as the university's buses or well-recognized cab firms, and consider using one of the multiple personal safety apps that are now available. These allow your friends to see your location and track you home safely. Agree on one together, in your friendship group, and all download it so you can help each other to stay safe.

TOP TIPS FOR STAYING SAFE AT NIGHT

- Walk with confidence, exude an assertive manner and keep your head up, being alert to your surroundings (don't wear headphones in both ears)
- Vary your routes and avoid being predictable
- Stick to well-lit areas and try to stay with friends
- If you feel that someone is threatening you, scream 'Fire!' and attract attention if possible
- Do not walk home after a night out and make sure you have plans for safe transport home

Sexual Safety and Consent

In an ideal world, we wouldn't have to think about such things as keeping ourselves safe from sexual assault or even rape. But the world is not ideal, and without any implication of victim blaming, it is really important to do what you can to keep yourself safe from assault no matter what your gender, as it can happen to anyone.

Definition of Rape

According to the Sexual Offences Act 2003 in England and Wales, the Sexual Offences Act (Scotland) 2009 and the Sexual Offences (Northern Ireland) Order 2008: A rape is when a person uses their penis without consent to penetrate the vagina, mouth, or anus of another person. Legally, a person without a penis cannot commit rape, but a female may be guilty of rape if they assist a male perpetrator in an attack.

In the US, according to RAINN (Rape, Abuse & Incest National Network): Rape is a form of sexual assault, but not all sexual assault is rape. The term rape is often used as a legal definition to specifically include sexual penetration without consent ... the FBI defines rape as "penetration, no matter how slight, of the vagina or anus with any body part or object, or oral penetration by a sex organ of another person, without the consent of the victim." To see how your state legally defines rape and other forms of sexual assault, visit RAINN's State Law Database: rainn.org.

Definition of Sexual Assault

According to the Sexual Offences Act 2003 in England and Wales, the Sexual Offences Act (Scotland) 2009 and the Sexual Offences (Northern Ireland) Order 2008: Sexual assault is when a person is coerced or physically forced to engage against their will, or when a person, male or female, touches another person sexually without their consent. Touching can be done with any part of the body or with an object. Sexual penetration is when a person (male or female) penetrates the vagina or anus of another person with any part of their body or an object without that person's consent.

In the US, according to RAINN: The term sexual assault refers to sexual contact or behavior that occurs without explicit consent of the victim. Some forms of sexual assault include:

- Attempted rape
- Fondling or unwanted sexual touching
- Forcing a victim to perform sexual acts, such as oral sex or penetrating the perpetrator's body
- Penetration of the victim's body, also known as rape

The legal definitions for terms like rape, sexual assault, and sexual abuse vary from state to state. See how each state legally defines these crimes by visiting RAINN's State Law Database. No matter what term you use, consent often plays an important role in determining whether an act is legally considered a crime (RAINN.org, 2019).

Huge advances have been made in recent years to raise awareness of the "consent conversation" and to bring such topics out into the open. Great resources for students are now available; they can teach you more about what consent means, and how to be a positive bystander ("bystander intervention training" teaches you how to recognize potentially harmful situations and turn them into positive outcomes by your choice of actions).

Your uni may well offer some online courses and modules in these topics and it's strongly encouraged that you take advantage of them, as well as encourage friends and flatmates to do so. The more everyone learns about it, the sooner our culture will shift to being safer for all of us.

TOP TIPS FOR STAYING SEXUALLY SAFE

- Know your sexual limits and stick to them
- Have a code word/phrase or number you can say/text to friends or family for help
- Don't be afraid to say no and hurt someone's feelings – be confident and clear or, if necessary, lie to get out of the situation
- Trust your instincts and leave any situation in which you feel unsafe
- This is not your fault; don't feel pressured or allow yourself to be convinced to do anything you don't want to do
- Consent is all about communication and you can withdraw it at any time
- Consent is a clear "yes" and *not* saying "no" does not mean you have consented to anything
- One thing does *not* have to lead to another
- Just because you have had sex with someone in the past, that does not imply consent for the next time

There is a lot more information about consent and sexual activity available on reliable websites and in the resources section of this book. But the key is to be alert to possibly tricky situations. Look after yourself and your friends, and if you do need help or support after an assault, then know that there are a lot of good people out there who want to help you. Help is available through your student or local health service support teams.

Mental Health Awareness

Although discussions around mental health are now more mainstream, in some cultures and areas, mental health issues can carry an unwarranted stigma. It isn't uncommon for doctors to see students from all sorts of backgrounds for whom mental health had never really been recognized as the real and important issue that it is. As one student put it:

> "I'm from a really conservative background and even if I knew about mental health via leaflets and websites, I don't think I would've taken it seriously because I've grown up with the idea that mental health isn't really a thing."

This can mean that many students experience various symptoms – such as low or flat mood, poor sleep, anxiety, recurrent negative or difficult thoughts, self-harm and eating issues – for years without realizing that they might have a mental health condition – or perhaps an emotional difficulty that could in fact be treated or supported. They don't realize that mental health can become *ill* health in the same way that physical health can become ill health.

The Relief of Seeking and Getting Help

It can be a huge relief when students discover that what they have been feeling is a well-recognized condition with a name and treatment options, and that often the right kind of talking therapy is what is needed. Some feel enormous pressure taken off them as they try a medication they never knew existed, and they "find themselves" again and a cloud of emotional negativity is lifted.

This may be the first time that they have spoken to someone about their symptoms. Also, as they move away from their families, and sometimes their countries or cultures, they have the opportunity to think about what is happening for them in a fresh light, with a different interpretation. They come to see that their struggles are not their fault and that sometimes they have a medical condition they cannot simply "snap out of" and can no longer ignore.

They seek advice and expert support, and new paths to recovery open up – with often transformational effects.

Be open to looking for and accepting help from others, whether that's a peer or a professional. It's important to talk about mental health and continue to make it a non-taboo subject.

Where Can You Get Help?

> "Nothing is more important than your health and wellbeing. Seeking help is the best decision and is not 'weak' and you should never let academic work take priority over your wellbeing."

The simple answer to this is to approach the university's professional student support services and ask for help, whether that is via a single point-of-entry "hub" or help desk, via their website, or via their counselling service.

You can also approach the local doctor or student health services. In the UK, many areas have psychological services that are available for free to the general public, so search online for "free NHS local psychology services" and book yourself an assessment.

And in the UK, it's free of charge! Not all students realize that this support is free and available to all registered students. In the US, most on-campus counselling services are free or at a reduced fee compared to off-campus counselling options through your insurance.

"If you have low mood or feel suicidal, go to the doctor."

"Use the university's mental health services, tell someone how you're feeling, don't be too hard on yourself, and give yourself a break. It's not your fault."

"I wish I had known that mental health services were offered. I knew I had problems with anxiety and was receiving help before university, but I thought I would have no help at all once I started uni."

And it's important to address this comment from a worried student:

"There are services available, so do not be put off by the waiting lists. However, many, many people are still very reluctant to get help because they feel the services are so understaffed that they will have to wait ages for a session, or if they do get a session, they are taking that spot away from someone else."

There may be a wait for longer-term support, group work, or one-to-one counselling appointments, but most doctors can see you quickly if you say it is for a mental health issue, and especially if you are feeling particularly unwell, self-harming or suicidal.

You should never worry that other people might be more unwell than you, that you are in some way not deserving of the appointment, or that you are using up resources. That is what they are there for; they work with students because they like students and want to support them in their studies. They want to ensure that students are reaching their potential. They might well be busy, but they always want to hear from you if you are feeling unwell or suffering.

A final word from students about seeking help:

> "Access everything. Try everything until you have found something that helps."

Disabilities – Physical or Mental

In your first term, it is well worth finding out about the support available for students with disabilities and what is actually considered a disability. You may be surprised to find that something that you have been struggling with for years, such as a mental health issue, is in fact a disability that entitles you to additional funding and help in the form of advice, mentoring or technical support.

> "I wish I had known that anxiety was actually considered to be a disability."

All universities have professionally staffed departments dedicated to supporting students with disabilities. They provide a vast array of services and advice, not just for learning disabilities like dyslexia, but also for those with physical ill health as well as mental ill health. You may need to provide documentation from your doctor or a psychologist, but once the paperwork is completed, you can start to reap the benefits and really transform your experience. For example, you may be entitled to additional time for an exam, or to sit on your own to complete it.

You should know that learning disabilities, like dyslexia, are common, and any difficulties with academic skills and performance should be followed up as quickly as possible. They should be addressed with a dedicated person from the university disability team.

In Summary

Be proactive in getting the support you need from disability and other uni services.

This first term can be a whirlwind of new experiences, so the message here is about proactive self-care. It is a crucial skill for wellbeing throughout life. This period will throw up challenges, so take positive action and seek help from the university's professional teams. If you are struggling, please ask for help.

CHAPTER 6

HOLIDAYS AND SELF-CARE

Holidays

The end of the first half of your school year has arrived. You crawl, exhausted, onto the coach, train, or plane, or into the car to go home for a few weeks of well-deserved and much-needed rest.

The holidays can be a wonderful opportunity to reconnect with family and friends at home, rest, eat nice food and do a bit of studying for exams. But they are not a haven for everyone.

For some students, going home can mean returning to a scene of conflict, to warring parents, to responsibilities of caring for someone, to controlling or abusive environments, or to isolation or emotional triggers. Not all homes are warm, welcoming and supportive.

Students have told doctors about their mental health medication being thrown away by upset parents who have discovered it. They've told of refusals to acknowledge their psychological condition as a "real thing". Students may come from a culture where their lifestyle or personal choices are frowned upon, or where they feel unable to be themselves with regards to gender or sexuality issues.

Conflicting Emotions

Returning home can bring up all sorts of conflicting emotions, from the significant to the mundane, such as wanting to be treated as an adult but having your parents treat you as the child you were when you left home.

In this situation, it can help to bring the issue up in a non-confrontational way with specific examples (such as the hour you might like to return home after a night out, if that has caused discussion), while offering to do things to help around the house – food shopping, laundry and so on. This way you're not treating the family home like the residence hall or a hotel.

Being thoughtful about how you fit back into the home when your family may only have just adjusted to your absence can help, along with spending time with other relatives, checking how your family are feeling, and asking how life is for them. Things may have changed or been difficult since you left, but they may have avoided sharing this with you so as not to distract you from your studies.

The key to a successful holiday period – if there are not significant issues such as those relating to severe disagreement over gender, sexuality or personal issues – is to spend time together *and* apart, to give everyone space to adjust while having time to catch up and allow the family dynamics to equilibrate. Be thoughtful, help out and be sensitive to other people's feelings.

Assuming that is all going well, with a bit of self-care, the holidays can be a time to recover from the extremes of diet (and alcohol), sleep disturbance, and the general assault on the human body that is student life.

It's time to get back in shape, eat fresh food, exercise and get fit for the term ahead!

What if You Don't or Can't "Go Home" for the Holidays?

There can be various reasons why students don't leave university at holiday times. They may not have a home to return to; perhaps they've been in foster care or are homeless. They could be international students for whom it is too expensive or challenging to travel. Maybe they'd rather avoid a conflict or difficult scenario, or perhaps their room at home is now in use by someone else, leaving them without a place to stay.

The university will likely be able to help support all these students in different ways, *if they are made aware of the situation*. They can often arrange homestays with local families, accommodation in residences, trips to enjoy local activities such as Christmas markets, day-to-day support from welfare or chaplaincy staff, and social media groups for all the students to link up if they wish to connect with others in the same circumstances.

The key here is that if you would like to connect with others over the holidays, and keep busy or try something new, then talk to the university support services *in advance* and allow them to help you achieve that.

Self-Care

> "Schedule a few hours in, spread over each week, where you do something active or self-care-ish that isn't remotely related to your course."

Great advice, for both term time and holidays, of course, so ...

Let's play Self-Care Bingo! For this activity you need to draw a 5 x 5 (3 x 3 is fine too!) square.

Then think of things that make you feel happy, warm, contented, energized and relaxed. Write them in the squares. For example, "Listen to a podcast or [name of song]", "Bake cakes", "Watch box set/Netflix", "Do a home manicure", "Work out" or "Go outside".

I'm sure you can think of lots more that are personal to you and will lift your spirits. They might involve other people too, so you might include "Call a friend", or "Go for a walk with [friend's name]". Petting your dog or hamster counts too!

Once you have created your bingo card, you can put it somewhere ready for days back at university, when you might need a little more support or feel a bit down or alone.

You can play by choosing which activities you feel like doing that day. If you have a good friend, they can play too, with the aim of focusing on having a day that lifts the spirits.

In Summary

Looking after yourself is important, and there are lots of practical ways that you can do this. It's critical to remember that student life is not just about term time, and that the holidays can bring their own challenges. They are not necessarily full of fun family or travel experiences and they're not always easy to fill with internships and great career-related opportunities. Sometimes getting through the holidays is a job in itself, and preparing for that possibility may help you to manage that task a little more easily.

CHAPTER 7

GETTING INTO THE RHYTHM OF STUDENT LIFE

The second half of the school year can be a rollercoaster of activities. Exams, deadlines, assignments, new activities, thinking about housing for next year – all of these pressures and more can suddenly pile up if you're not ready, looking after yourself and firing on all cylinders.

The key to success here is pacing yourself, preparation and sleep!

Sleep

> "Make sure you have a balance of time with others and time by yourself, and get enough sleep."

Missing out on sleep can have a "catastrophic effect" on your health and wellbeing. Healthcare professionals often tell students that rather than resort to study drugs as many do (to stay awake and work longer), they would be better off getting a good night's sleep and then having a cup of coffee in the morning.

So How Do You Get a Good Night's Sleep?

Well first of all, before we get into the "sleep rules", it's important to understand that sleep is a habit. So if it has been "broken" and you are not sleeping well, or you have been sleeping in the day and up all night, then it will take time to reset your internal body clock and get into a good habit. About six weeks of following the sleep rules should do it, but if you're still struggling after that, talk to a doctor or therapist about it. Don't suffer in silence.

Insomnia and disrupted sleep patterns can be absolute torture, as trainee doctors and others who go for days without sleep and work nights will tell you. You are strongly urged not to ignore this essential bodily function!

TOP SLEEP TIPS

- Try to go to bed and get up at the same time every day, Monday to Sunday. If necessary, use your alarm to set the routine!
- Try to be asleep when it's dark and awake when it's light, although within reason, for example between 11pm and 8am, but not sleeping in the daytime or staying up all night to work. You need about nine hours' sleep on average as a young adult.
- If you have to nap in the day, then do it before 3pm.
- Stop all work and turn off all screens one hour before bedtime.
- Spend that hour winding down, chatting with a friend, listening to quiet music, having a hot bath, reading quietly, or watching TV (nothing too scary or exciting!).
- Exercise in the daytime before about 6pm, and don't have caffeine or alcohol late in the evening or eat any heavy meals. Light snacks are okay.
- Create a gadget-free zone – lights that might blink at night, notifications lighting up the room, and clocks that you can stare at are all no-nos.
- Don't lie in bed awake for hours. If you can't get off to sleep, get up and do a relaxing activity for a while. When you feel sleepier, try again to sleep.

Stick to these rules for about four to six weeks, and if that isn't working, check out CBT-I (Cognitive Behavioural Therapy for Insomnia). It is evidence-based and designed to improve sleep. Also make time to talk to a professional about how you are doing. There may be other things you can try that can help to improve your sleep and mood.

Exercise

Look, it's not exactly news that exercise is good for us, or that we should try to stay active on a regular basis. Life is too short to repeat the obvious and tell you what you already know. But in terms of student life, even the most dedicated school athletes can find it hard to stay fit once they hit the campus!

Universities provide a huge range of opportunities for exercise, sport and activity, ranging from top-level teams to beginners. Many are showcased at the Welcome Week fair, but you can check them out all year round. Residences and the student union will host groups and classes, whether you're into Zumba or historical walking tours. The choices are endless, and hopefully there is something for everyone (including women-only classes if that is a priority for you), but if you are not naturally inclined to break a sweat or move at faster than a gentle stroll, at least make it easy for yourself:

TOP EXERCISE TIPS

- Take the stairs rather than the elevators
- Walk or cycle instead of taking the bus or driving
- If you have to sit at a desk all day or be in lectures for long hours, then make sure you take breaks to get outside and walk around the block at the very least

Screen Time

We all spend a lot of time on our phones, and many of us likely have a love–hate relationship with the technology that surrounds us daily.

No one is suggesting that you stop using your phone, tablet, or laptop, but it may be worth taking a moment to reflect on *how much* you use it, what your attention span is like, and what you could be doing instead of being on your screen, with the aim of perhaps studying more effectively and achieving more with your time.

Studies have shown that 17-year-olds spend around six hours a day of their leisure time (not studying) on their screens (Monitoring the Future, 2013–2015), and that their attention span is about 19 seconds on average before they switch tasks on their laptops (Yeykelis, Cummings and Reeves, 2014).

Take a moment to reflect on those facts and compare your own screen time. You may want to consider spending some of that texting/surfing/video chatting time on activities with other humans, reading, or doing something active that will make you feel better emotionally. You might also like to try using tech to control your tech use, such as apps to reduce or manage your screen time if necessary.

The Effects of More Screen Time on Our Lives

Sadly, research is finding that *the more time we spend on our screens, the less happy we are*. More screen time causes more anxiety, depression, loneliness and less emotional connection (Tromholt, 2016 and Sherman, Michikyan and Greenfield, 2013). It also makes us more likely to be overweight.

On the other hand, spending time with other humans face to face makes us feel better, happier and healthier.

It is important to acknowledge the significant support many people also draw on, via online groups, social media, and personal networks, to keep themselves from being isolated or to meet those with shared interests. Screen time is absolutely *not all bad*, but as with most things in life, a little bit of balance goes a long way.

So every now and then, give yourself a break, get out and see people, connect with the outside world. Take time to read books (to improve your attention span), and exercise, which will in turn help you to study more effectively for your degree.

Smoking

Doctors often find that trying to get students to give up smoking when they have often only just started is *really* hard!

Students definitely smoke in fewer numbers these days, which is great because it really is bad for your health in so many ways (it damages your lungs, heart, kidneys, eyes, brain ... the list goes on) but some students obviously do still smoke and often it is used as a stress-relief mechanism. So if you are a smoker, then maybe it is worth having a think about *why* you smoke, and whether there might be a healthier alternative.

You could also think about the money you would save, and put it towards something specific, so that it really does feel like a positive achievement when you quit and have some cash (or a treat) to show for it!

Help to give up smoking is available through your doctor's office, so ask at reception. If you're in the UK, look for your local Stop Smoking Service on the NHS website. In the US, check out the CDC website for resources.

You are more likely to be successful at giving up smoking with support or professional help, so take the time to look after yourself and book yourself an appointment at a time when you don't feel too stressed and are ready to make the change (i.e., not right before exams!).

Drugs

Students use drugs for many different reasons – to party, sure, but also to self-medicate (to help with their own distress, anxiety, depression, etc.), to cope with exam stress specifically, to study (see later in this chapter for information on study drugs) and to manage social anxiety, to name but a few.

The offer of drugs may come at any time, of course, but when the work is piling up, the exams become real and the deadlines loom, drug use may seem like an option to help you cope. However, if you are struggling with your wellbeing or you are under pressure with work, then, as one of my students said very clearly, "Don't drink. Don't go anywhere near drugs."

So, if this is the situation for you and you are stressed, try to avoid using any drugs and talk to someone about getting help. Get into a healthy sleep and exercise routine. Eat some fresh food daily, and make a study timetable you can follow, maybe with a friend, to keep you on track and feeling like *you can do this*.

If you are using drugs and are finding it hard to stop but you would like to, you are not alone. It's hard to get a real sense of how common drug use is among university students, with two UK-based studies in 2018 giving differing results. The NUS report *Taking the Hit* showed that 56 per cent of 3,000 respondents had ever used drugs, but the Higher Education Policy Institute (HEPI) report of 1,000 students showed only 39% had. More interesting perhaps were the differing attitudes of the students in the two surveys about whether or not drug use is harmful to mental health. Despite a mountain of scientific evidence to the contrary (drugabuse.gov), two-thirds of NUS respondents who thought that drug use had affected their health said it had done so in a positive way, improving their mental health.

In the US, statistics are similar to one of those reports. SAMHSA (Substance Abuse and Mental Health Services Administration) surveyed 18- to 25-year-olds and found that 39% of them had used illicit drugs in the past year.

The fact is that drugs are not good for you, and if you are using them to cope with stress or anxiety, then please talk to a professional healthcare worker. They are there to help you with whatever underlying issues are causing your worries. They want to help you to deal with them in a healthier and more effective way.

Midterm Blues

Whether they happen in the first or second part of the year the midterm blues are all too real for some students. You hit the ground running as the term starts, full of energy, drive, enthusiasm, and ideas, then as the weeks progress, you slump, overcome with exhaustion, burning the candle at both ends and too tired to do anything properly. It can be a bit of a shock, but it's common and nothing to panic about.

This is a good moment to review that Self-Care Bingo square you created. Plan a few early nights to get your sleep pattern back on track, or book a day out in your diary to just do things that you enjoy and don't involve any work.

Take a Day Off!

Taking a break from work can be essential to allow your brain to recover from all the studying, exams and essays, to think in new ways about work or projects and to approach your next assignment feeling refreshed.

If you think you might need help to plan your workload or manage all the competing demands, then ask your advisor, tutor or someone in your academic department for help. Check out what study skills workshops and learning events are being held.

If the institution only has "one job", this is it. They are there to help you get your degree, so take advantage of all their resources and get the support you need!

In Summary

The second half of the school year can be more of a bumpy ride than you might have expected, so it's really important to keep to a good sleep routine, exercise when you can, and if you have been coping with the stress or "self-medicating" by gaming online, smoking, or taking drugs of any sort, then please take some time to sort yourself out and look after yourself.

If you're feeling the pressure and it's starting to affect you and your work, then help is out there – including from the support services, your academic tutors and department staff, and your family and friends, as well as online and in books. You are not alone, so please reach out.

CHAPTER 8

END-OF-YEAR ISSUES

When you think about the end-of-year, exams are probably the main thing on your mind, but perhaps you also start to think about holidays, jobs, next year's potential living issues, graduation, study abroad and so on. All of these things can bring both a sense of achievement and a sense of adventure ... or possibly anxiety.

You've made it this far. The end of the academic year is in sight and a new chapter is about to begin. But for some it can feel a bit overwhelming; the fear of failing the exams is high and the worry about change (nobody likes change!) is real and can make you nervous.

Living Arrangement Issues

On the subject of next year's housing, it can be worth taking a moment to consider the issues that can arise with housemates. University is a unique opportunity to meet people from all over the world, from multiple cultural and social backgrounds, and it can be a fantastic way to make new friends.

When you move in together, it can test those friendships in a way that hanging out in the bar or living in residence halls never did. Suddenly, you have bills to pay together, cleaning to do, maintenance to be aware of, and responsibilities – and not everyone shares the same attitudes and values toward these important (if dull!) tasks. Despite the plethora of amusing blogs about clichéd housemate stereotypes, it can sometimes cause a serious degree of stress, not least if a friend has a mental health issue which can then impact on other housemates.

Living with People with Mental Health Issues

If this is a scenario you are concerned about, talk to someone about it (preferably a member of the university mental health teams) and get advice. You are not the person's carer or next of kin, and other people need to help you to support them. As a friend you don't have a confidentiality boundary, nor should you feel pressured to keep things secret. Please talk to the professionals if you need help.

If the issues are more related to differing approaches to rent/bills/care of the property/partying habits and so on, then think carefully about how to approach the tricky housemate and use your best "conflict resolution" skills to have a difficult conversation.

TOP TIPS ON ADDRESSING CONFLICT

- Find a calm time and place to talk.
- Use active listening (really hear what they are saying and try not to judge them).
- Be fair.
- Solve the problem and don't attack each other.
- Accept responsibility.
- Be direct.
- Find common ground.
- Try to find a shared future aim or solution (where do you both want to be?).
- Agree your mutual shared benefit (negotiate/compromise).
- If you can't compromise, maybe agree to differ and move on.
- If the conversation gets too heated, take time out and come back to it.

Using this approach might avoid the breakdown of a good friendship and pre-empt a difficult situation.

Pre-exam Panic

Remember! The end of the year can be a stressful time, and you are not alone. Pre-exam season can be particularly fraught for students, so make use of any review classes, extra seminars or lectures, groups for study skills, or de-stressing sessions involving sports or even puppies! They are all there to help you succeed and stay well.

Even if you think you have left it too late to get help and that no one can help you now, it is genuinely never too late.

Universities have systems in place to aid and assist students whatever the situation, and even if you might need to take time out and re-sit a year, you would be one of many, *many* students who do this each year. Similarly, if you are ill on the day of an exam or during your exam, as long as you let people know and engage with the processes, there are plenty of options to solve the problem.

Study Drugs

It's at this point that you may, if you haven't already, consider trying study drugs or "smart" drugs.

Exam studying feels like a mountain to climb, there aren't enough hours in the day, exams are looming, and deadlines feel far too real. The idea of using something to "boost" your performance would hardly be new, and it's believed that James Bond, JFK, and Hitler were all fans of using prescription medications in non-prescription ways to increase their alertness or effectiveness.

However, taking prescription medications when they have not been prescribed for you, or for a purpose other than which they were designed for, brings significant risks. For example, students sometimes take medication designed to treat those with diagnosed Attention Deficit Disorder in the mistaken belief that it will allow them to improve the quality of their work, study more effectively, write a better essay and so on. The evidence to date shows that in healthy individuals functioning at optimum level, these (and other "smart" medications) will make *no improvement* to cognitive functioning and may in fact impair performance (BMA.org.uk, 2015).

Students also commonly take a medication usually used for narcolepsy (when you fall asleep spontaneously at inappropriate times) to keep them awake for excessive periods of time, to allow them to work for longer. They will definitely keep you awake for a long time, but as we have mentioned before, sleep deprivation is bad for your health and can even lead to hallucinations, among other side effects. Sleep is also crucial for your memory to function.

Needless to say, these medications have significant side effects and possibly long-term complications in those for whom they have not been prescribed. It is these unpleasant side effects that usually bring students to doctors' consulting rooms: palpitations, diarrhoea, headaches and an inability to sleep at all.

So when someone offers you a "quick fix" to "boost" your study, bear this in mind: it is risky, potentially dangerous, and – most ironic of all – "smart" drugs don't make you smarter!

Another quick word about alcohol – it is really normal for humans to find ways to cope when things are difficult, and we all use a variety of "substances" with which to "self-medicate." Food, cigarettes, drugs and alcohol are all common sources of distraction for us when we are stressed. If you notice that you are starting to "use" any of these more or relying on them to get you through challenging times, try to stop and ask yourself *why* you are turning to them. There will be other things you can do instead that might be better, such as exercise, talking to friends and family about your stress or relaxation techniques.

Exams, Assignments and Academic Pressure

Clearly, academic pressure will have been something to think about before this point in the school year, but it's covered here because this is when healthcare providers see the largest number of students about work-related worries and stress.

When Does Academic Stress Warrant Intervention?

First of all, it is important to say that it is entirely normal to feel anxious and worried about exams. Our bodies are designed to give us a rush of adrenaline when we are stressed, to help focus the mind and be on our toes. So there is no need to worry about worrying!

However, if you feel more than manageably anxious (for example, if you haven't slept for days, you have stopped eating, you are losing weight, you cry all the time or you no longer enjoy the activities you did before, then please talk with a professional about how you are feeling. This will give you a sense of whether you have moved beyond normal anxiety about work to being unwell and requiring help.

You don't need to see a doctor or counsellor if you can't sleep the night before a specific exam, if you feel sick just before it or if you feel on edge about it. This is all very normal and there's nothing we can do. But if you are shaking, sweating and having palpitations and are physically a bit overwhelmed by your "fight or flight" reaction, it may be worth discussing this "performance-related anxiety". You could consider learning relaxation techniques or even taking beta blockers (which don't cloud the mind, but block the adrenaline that is rushing to your sweat glands).

And Most Serious of All ... Suicide Risk

There is no doubt that students worry about money, making friends and eating healthily, among other things, but academic stress looms very large for many and can sadly even be a factor in student suicide, with rates of suicide peaking in exam months such as April and May (NCISH, 2018).

This underlines how important it is not to ignore your distress if you are finding work or life overwhelming, worried about letting people down or frightened of "failure".

There is *always* something that the university support services, health teams and counsellors can do to help, so even if *you* have never considered what all the options are, it is likely that they will have come across a similar situation before and will be able to offer hope and a practical plan.

GET SOME HELP

Immediate help is always available if you feel like this. Speak to your doctor or go to the local hospital emergency department. In the UK, dial the emergency phone number 999, or contact Samaritans for free by phone or text (available 24/7 at 116 123). In the US, dial 1 (800) 273-8255 or visit suicidepreventionlifeline.org.

TOP TIPS FOR EXAM PREPARATION

- Don't leave it all till the last minute – plan your revision and stick to the plan.
- Use flow charts, diagrams, and visual aids – people learn brilliantly with images to help them.
- Go over old exam papers and questions.
- Explain topics to people who don't study them with you; having to explain something helps you to understand it better.
- Take breaks for 10 minutes at least. Stretch, walk, get outside, and get some vitamin D every 60 to 90 minutes.
- Eat sensible healthy food and stay hydrated. And don't skip breakfast on the day of the exam!
- Plan for the day of the exam. Where and when is it happening? (Yes, doctors and nurses have been asked for a note by someone who missed their exam because they "got lost on the way". But no, they didn't write one!)
- Get lots of sleep the night before.
- Vary the location of your studying for most effective learning (Carey, 2015) and reduced anxiety sitting the exam in an unfamiliar location.
- Don't just copy out lecture notes – read them, then write down what you remember for better long-term recall.
- Work in a group and explain things to each other, if you like studying with others.

Summer Holidays

You've made it!

You've survived the year, the exams and the emotional roller coaster that university can be.

And here you are, ready for the holidays.

As we said in the chapter about holidays in general, many students may look upon the summer with apprehension rather than anticipation, but for everyone it will likely bring a change of routine, a change of scene perhaps, and opportunities to earn money, travel, see old friends and catch up with family. But it may also bring a feeling of unease or worry.

Students who have happily discovered their identity at university and been accepted as themselves may not be the person their family remembers, and there may be resulting conflict or some adaptation required on both sides.

It may be difficult to take a new romantic partner home with you or to explain your sexuality to those who have known you since childhood.

Whatever the scenario, it is important to think ahead as the term progresses, as your final months of study are notoriously short, and the holidays will arrive before you think it possible.

TOP TIPS FOR THE SUMMER BREAK

- Apply for internships and jobs well in advance.
- Drop hints about any changes in you or your lifestyle to those back home.
- Make travel plans.
- Think ahead to the next academic year, even if the basics, like accommodation and course modules, are in place.
- It may be worth speaking to those in the year above you and asking for any tips or what they wish they had known in advance.

There are many things you can do if you feel like the holidays are stretching ahead and you're not sure what to do. It doesn't have to be ice cream and Netflix all the way, though that is obviously fine for your days off!

Summer Activities

Think about volunteering at a local charity. It will be great experience, help you meet people, and give you something to put on that all-important CV or résumé.

If you can, learn to drive and get independent. It's a life skill and is particularly useful for some careers, too.

Apply to get work experience somewhere that interests you, especially if you're not sure what you want to do with your life. For example, do you wonder what it would be like to be a music therapist or a veterinary nurse? If so, contact local people who do these roles and ask if you can shadow them or even just have a chat if it's too complicated to go into their workplace.

You can always make a start on any course reading lists for next year and plan a couple of festival visits (not necessarily the big, expensive ones) with friends while you decide what to do with the rest of your break.

The summer holidays are a great opportunity to take a break, recover from university life, get your health back, travel long distances to see the world or earn a decent bit of cash for the year ahead. But most of all, you've earned these experiences!

In Summary

Exams are the main stress for most students, though living arrangements and holiday or graduation plans can run a close second. It is really important not to underestimate how much pressure students can feel at exam time and it can have a particularly significant effect on mental health. So, if you are struggling, you are most definitely not alone and it is *never* too late to seek support and advice.

Don't ignore the stress or believe that no one can help you now. And if you are feeling desperate or you're even thinking about suicide, then the support teams and healthcare professionals particularly want to reach out to you and tell you that there is *always* hope, that the university *can* help you, and that compassionate professionals are always available if you ask for help.

FINAL WORDS

In summary, you're in higher education to get a degree and have a good time doing it, while hopefully making some new friends and learning some new skills. The institutions are there to make sure that you achieve these things to the best of your ability, to help you fulfil your potential, and move on in the world having had a positive experience.

This book aims to support you in achieving these things while staying healthy and knowing a little bit more about how to stay well (and safe).

A little preparation before arrival, knowing more what to expect of each term, and understanding that sometimes things don't always play out quite as you'd expect (for example, the holidays) will mean that you can navigate your first year ready to study effectively, connect with other people, care for yourself and, importantly, have some fun!

University life may not be the "best days of your life", but it is a real opportunity to try new things, find your "tribe", stretch yourself, perhaps discover a secret talent and get a degree before you embark on your next adventure.

Five Ways to Staying Well

This is another great way to think about how to look after yourself all year round, but it's helpful to start practising in the holidays when you have the brain space to think about it.

The Five Ways to Wellbeing that are encouraged by the UK's NHS sets, out the five things we can all do to stay well:

1. **Connect** – this relates to connecting with other people. We are social creatures, and as humans, we do best when connected to others in positive ways.

2. **Be active** – staying active and exercising – even if it's just walking or strolling – is highly recommended for a healthy life.

3. **Take notice** – this refers to being aware of the world around you, of nature, of the activities you do, of your breathing, of what you eat. It is often associated with the practice of mindfulness (taking time to focus on the present moment and appreciate the sensations associated with it).

4. **Keep learning** – a good one for students, this is about keeping your brain active and healthy by always being curious and learning new things.

5. **Give** – this relates to the fact that helping others makes you feel better and happier too. So take the time to volunteer, help a friend and share what you have.

In reality, this way of approaching self-care and wellbeing means looking for ways to spend time with other people and finding activities that you enjoy. It doesn't mean making yourself train for marathons if you hate running, but it can mean going for a lovely walk outside, somewhere you enjoy. That might be a park, the woods, the beach, a market or any big, open space where you can see the sky. It is also about being aware of the world around you as you wander – the smells, the sounds, the colours, the feel of the ground under your feet, the touch of leaves on trees or clothes on stalls. It's about taking time to appreciate the world around you, reconnecting with it and being in that moment.

You could also look for ways to help and support others. That might be by giving your time or sharing your energy or abilities by volunteering locally. Hopefully, as a student, the aim to "keep learning" will be a given, but you might want to add something else into the mix. You could learn a new language, instrument, activity or skill. It's up to you, but all of these ways to stay well should lift your spirits and keep you feeling enthusiastic and on track for the new term.

TOP TIPS FOR STAYING WELL

1. Talk to family or friends for support.

2. There are lots of self-help options available: exercise, being around nature, nurturing a pet or plant, connecting with others and helping them too, as well as mindfulness techniques if you need a bit of "me time". You'll feel good for trying and there's always more help if you are struggling.

3. Your university will provide loads of free help, for example via the counselling, chaplaincy or wellbeing services.

4. Check in with the disability services team to see if you are entitled to support.

5. Use the free student counselling service at your institution.

6. Look at your university student health centre or student support services website as a first step, to see what they can offer.

7. If you are an international student, look out for the international student office.

8. Residences and halls will usually have staff and peer support teams focused on your wellbeing.

9. Peer mentors are hard at work in most universities – students supporting other students.

10. Many universities offer free online support too, so that's another option to consider if you aren't keen to talk face-to-face.

11. The student union is a great place to look for groups, clubs, societies, and wellbeing advice and help.

12. Don't forget that the security teams are available and often trained in mental health support. They are there to protect you and advise on personal safety. Some universities have their own police officers.

13. The sports, exercise and health teams in most universities are really active and keen to get students involved, whether for specific teams, individual sports or general activities to stay healthy.

14. On the academic side, your personal advisor or tutor should be the first port of call, the person to talk to if your work is worrying you or if there is anything you want to discuss. If they can't help you directly, then they can signpost you to the right person, give advice, listen and be proactive.

15. Your academic department will also be home to lots of lovely administrative staff who spend a lot of their time helping students. They will be a source of a huge variety of useful knowledge, so make sure you meet them early on and chat with them when you can – if they are not too busy at that moment.

16. The careers team can help with student jobs and holiday work as well as long-term career planning.

TOP TRANSITION TIPS FOR NEW STUDENTS

1. **Prepare:** Sit down with someone you trust and write a list of all your worries and concerns, so that you can start to address them together.

2. **Create an action plan:** Put all your worries or concerns into different categories, such as making friends, your studies, budgeting and living away from home, and make an action plan for each one, containing solutions for each worry.

3. **Organize your medical care:** If you need support for any health condition or disability, plan how you can get the care and support you need. A good starting point is to search your university's website for student support to look for information about available services.

4. **Register with a new doctor:** Check out your university's website to see if they have one on campus or whether they recommend a particular local practice.

5. **Medication:** If you take regular medications or need medical devices or equipment, plan what you need and get an appropriate supply of prescriptions in advance (to be agreed with your doctor) so you don't run out!

6. **Contact student support services:** If you have ongoing mental health issues, get in touch with student support services before you get to campus. They're there to support you and will do what they can to help. Phone or email them for advice and don't be shy in asking for help if you need it.

7. **Sort out ongoing care:** If you're under specialist care for conditions like asthma, diabetes or a mental health problem, register with a new doctor as soon as possible so that you can discuss ongoing care and possible referral to local services.

8. **Get comfortable:** Take a few things with you that remind you of home, like your coziest pajamas or your usual duvet and bedsheets instead of buying new ones. You could also make a playlist of your favourite songs and photos of family and friends for times when you need a boost.

9. **Look after your wellbeing:** Make a personal wellbeing plan of five things you can do every day and to help build your wellbeing. Include things in your plan like sleep, exercise, activities that you enjoy, something relaxing, socializing with friends, small treats, university societies and clubs, support from home and so on.

10. **Make a safety plan:** Sit down with someone you trust and make a plan of things you can do for yourself. Write down how you can get in touch with people you can ask for support if you ever feel low, get stressed or are struggling.

If you're worried or stressed after reading our tips, please talk to someone about how you are feeling, as you may need extra support.

Tips provided by **Dr Alys Cole-King** (on Twitter @ AlysColeKing) with input from **Dr Dominique Thompson**, Student Health Expert (@DrDomThompson, buzzconsulting. co.uk) and **Dr Knut Schroeder** (@DrKnut and @expertselfcare).

TOP TIPS FOR PARENTS OF NEW STUDENTS

1. **Cooking:** Teach them how to cook. Start with two or three simple recipes they can cook for themselves and others, which can help them make new friends.

2. **Laundry:** Teach them how to do their laundry. It's a simple and essential life skill – and it saves your own time!

3. **Healthcare:** Teach them where to get over-the-counter medicines and prescriptions, how to register and book a doctor's appointment and how to navigate the local healthcare system or emergency services if they're unwell.

4. **Budget:** Plan a budget for food shopping and other essentials. Instead of organizing food delivery, let them learn for themselves how to shop sensibly. Useful financial tips for students are available at blackbullion.com.

5. **First aid:** Teach them basic first aid and provide them with a small kit containing essentials like adhesive bandages, dressings or gauze, paper stitches and painkillers.

6. **Security:** Explain basic security measures, such as avoiding using cashpoints or ATMs at night, protecting drinks so they don't get spiked and keeping belongings safe. Ask them to download a mobile security app.

7. **Parental contacts:** Agree and plan in advance how often you'll contact each other and which medium you'll use, such as weekly phone calls or WhatsApp messages every other day. Allow some flexibility and don't expect daily contacts, so you won't get stressed if they oversleep and didn't check in.

8. **Drop-off:** Don't hang around too long when dropping them off. They need to get on and meet people and start blending in, not worry about you.

9. **Biscuits:** Take biscuits or cake (ideally low in sugar and fat, with gluten- and nut-free options) when droppingthem off to create an instant talking point with other new students and their parents.

10. **Coming home:** Allow at least four weeks before they come home, so they can meet people and don't miss out on early events that help them build connections that are key to feeling settled and part of the wider university community.

Tips provided by **Dr Alys Cole-King** (on Twitter @ AlysColeKing) with input from **Dr Dominique Thompson**, Student Health Expert (@DrDomThompson, buzzconsulting. co.uk) and **Dr Knut Schroeder** (@DrKnut and @expertselfcare).

ADDITIONAL RESOURCES

APPS

UK

- *Student Health App* – for all health matters
- Personal safety apps
- CBT-I apps – for insomnia
- *distrACT* – for information on, and support for, self-harm
- *Headspace* – for mindfulness
- *SAM (Self-help App for the Mind)* – for wellbeing

US

- *Better Stop Suicide* – for suicide prevention self-help
- *Headspace* – for mindfulness
- *MindKit* – for organization

WEBSITES

UK

- Student Minds (the UK national student mental health charity) **studentminds.org.uk**
- *Know Before You Go* **studentminds.org.uk/knowbeforeyougo.html**
- NHS support **nhs.uk**
- Financial advice **blackbullion.com**
- Financial advice **moneysavingexpert.com**
- Financial advice **savethestudent.org**
- The Mix (support for under-25s) **themix.org.uk**
- Mind **mind.org.uk** or call **0300 123 3393**
- Drug info **talktofrank.com**
- Alcohol info **www.drinkaware.co.uk**

- Addiction **wearewithyou.org.uk**
- Gambling and gaming addiction **www.gamequitters.com** and **www.gamanon.org.uk**
- Eating issues **www.network-ed.org.uk**
- ADHD **www.adhdfoundation.org.uk**
- Asperger's syndrome and autism **www.autism.org.uk**
- Gender diversity **www.mermaidsuk.org.uk**
- LGBTQ + **www.stonewall.org.uk**

US

- Mental Health America **mentalhealthamerica.net**
- Student mental health **activeminds.org**
- Addiction **shatterproof.org**
- Gambling and gaming addiction **ncpgambling.org**
- Eating issues **nationaleatingdisorders.org**
- ADHD **chadd.org**
- Asperger's syndrome and autism **autism-society.org**
- LGBTQ+ and gender issues **thetrevorproject.org**

BOOKS

- *How We Learn* by Benedict Carey
- *Study Skills Handbook* by Stella Cottrell
- *Why We Sleep* by Matthew Walker
- *Social Media and Mental Health: Handbook for Teens* by Dr Claire Edwards
- *Social Media and Mental Health: Handbook for Parents and Guardians* by Dr Claire Edwards

YOUTUBE

- Pooky Knightsmith Mental Health channel

REFERENCES

Bma.org.uk. (2015). *BMA - Cognitive enhancing drugs and the workplace*. [online] Available at: https://www.bma.org.uk/media/1068/bma_cognitive_enhancing_drugs_and_the_workplace_oct_2019.pdf [Accessed 12 July 2021].

Drugabuse.gov. (2017). *Mental Health Effects*. [online] Available at: https://www.drugabuse.gov/publications/health-consequences-drug-misuse/mental-health-effects [Accessed 12 July 2021].

GOV.UK. (2008). *Five ways to mental wellbeing*. [online] Available at: https://www.gov.uk/government/publications/five-ways-to-mental-wellbeing [Accessed 12 July 2021].

HEPI. (2018). *Most students think taking illegal drugs causes problems for users as well as society and want their universities to take a tougher stance*. [online] Available at: https://www.hepi.ac.uk/2018/06/12/students-think-taking-illegal-drugs-causes-problems-users-well-society-want-universities-take-tougher-stance/ [Accessed 12 July 2021].

Holloway, K. and Bennett, T. (2017). *Characteristics and correlates of drug use and misuse among university students in Wales: a survey of seven universities*. Addiction Research & Theory, 26(1), pp.11–19.

Hughes, G., Massey, F. and Williams, S. (2017). *An investigation of the views, understanding, knowledge, experience and attitudes of sixth form teachers in regard to the preparedness of their students for the transition to university*. [online] Derby.openrepository.com. Available at: http://derby.openrepository.com/derby/handle/10545/621721 [Accessed 12 July 2021].

John, E. (2017). *Adult drinking habits in Great Britain - Office for National Statistics*. [online] Ons.gov.uk. Available at: https://www.ons.gov.uk/peoplepopulationandcommunity/healthandsocialcare/drugusealcoholandsmoking/bulletins/opinionsandlifestylesurveyadultdrinkinghabits ingreatbritain/2017 [Accessed 12 July 2021].

Medlineplus.gov. (2012). *Tips for Getting A Good Night's Sleep*, NIH MedlinePlus the Magazine. [online] Available at: https://medlineplus.gov/magazine/issues/summer15/articles/summer15pg22.html [Accessed 12 July 2021].

NCISH. (2018). *Annual report 2018: England, Northern Ireland, Scotland and Wales*. [online] Available at: https://sites.manchester.ac.uk/ncish/reports/annual-report-2018-england-northern-ireland-scotland-and-wales/ [Accessed 12 July 2021].

Nus.org.uk. (2018). *New survey shows trends in student drinking*. [online] Available at: https://www.nus.org.uk/en/news/press-releases/new-survey-shows-trends-in-student-drinking/ [Accessed 12 July 2021].

Nus.org.uk. (2018). *Taking the Hit: student drug use and how institutions respond*. [online] Available at: https://www.nusconnect.org.uk/resources/taking-the-hit-student-drug-use-and-how-institutions-respond [Accessed 12 July 2021].

Sherman, L., Michikyan, M. and Greenfield, P. (2013). *The effects of text, audio, video, and in-person communication on bonding between friends*. [online] Available at: https://cyberpsychology.eu/article/view/4285 [Accessed 12 July 2021].

Studentminds.org.uk. (2018). *Know Before You Go*. [online] Available at: https://www.studentminds.org.uk/uploads/3/7/8/4/3784584/180813_kbyg_interactive.pdf [Accessed 12 July 2021].

Thompson, D. and Cole-King, A. (2018). *10 top transition and wellbeing tips for new students starting uni*. [online] Available at: https://buzzconsulting.co.uk/docs/Top-Tips-for-young-people-starting-uni.pdf [Accessed 12 July 2021].

Tromholt, M. (2016). *The Facebook Experiment: Quitting Facebook Leads to Higher Levels of Well-Being*. Cyberpsychol Behav Soc Netw. 2016 Nov;19(11): 661–666. doi: 10.1089/cyber.2016.0259 [Accessed 12 July 2021].

Waters, L. (2018). *Putting the rise of STIs in England into context*. [online] Pharmaceutical Journal. Available at: https://pharmaceutical-journal.com/article/opinion/putting-the-rise-of-stis-in-england-into-context [Accessed 12 July 2021].

Yeykelis, L., Cummings, J. and Reeves, B. (2014). *Multitasking on a Single Device: Arousal and the Frequency, Anticipation, and Prediction of Switching Between Media Content on a Computer*. Journal of Communication. 64(1), pp 167–192.

NOTES

NOTES

NOTES

NOTES

NOTES

ABOUT US

Welbeck Balance publishes books dedicated to changing lives. Our mission is to deliver life-enhancing books to help improve your wellbeing so that you can live your life with greater clarity and meaning, wherever you are on life's journey. Our Trigger books are specifically devoted to opening up conversations about mental health and wellbeing.

Welbeck Balance and Trigger are part of the Welbeck Publishing Group – a globally recognized independent publisher based in London. Welbeck are renowned for our innovative ideas, production values and developing long-lasting content. Our books have been translated into over 30 languages in more than 60 countries around the world.

If you love books, then join the club and sign up to our newsletter for exclusive offers, extracts, author interviews and more information.

www.welbeckpublishing.com   www.triggerhub.org

🐦 welbeckpublish   🐦 Triggercalm
📷 welbeckpublish   📷 Triggercalm
📘 welbeckuk   📘 Triggercalm